MY GRANDMOTHER'S PATCHWORK QUILT

A Book and Pocketful of Patchwork Pieces

Janet Bolton

Tango BOOKS

Not so long ago my grandmother gave me a very special present. It was the dolls' quilt she had made when she was a young girl living with her brother and parents on the farm.

My brother and me on the farm.

On winter evenings, after she got home from
the one-room school and did her chores,
Grandmother would collect her sewing basket.
She would sit by the fire and work on this
small quilt for her dolls.

The cockerel crowed outside my window every morning at six o'clock, waking me up. I poured some water from my jug into the bowl on my washstand, quickly washed my face and hands and jumped into my clothes. It was cold in my room.

Grandmother's quilt was a record of the animals on the farm. It was made lovingly from little scraps of homespun material: her father's old shirts, her mother's worn-out aprons and tablecloths. She kept the scraps in her sewing basket along with a thimble, a pair of scissors, different coloured threads and a needle.

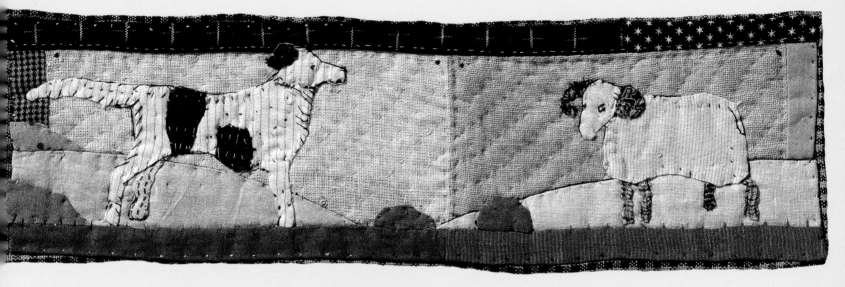

From my window I could see the sheepdog beginning to round up the flock of sheep. Each spring, at lambing time, we had many baby lambs.

Sometimes, when her mother bought cloth from a big bolt at the general store for a new dress or shirt, my grandmother got a small piece to add to her quilt.

When my mother called, I would hurry downstairs, passing Puss on the way. Puss always waited for me in the hall to say good morning. We all had our jobs to do, and Puss's was to catch mice.

Grandmother drew pictures on paper of the different animals she wanted to sew. Then she copied each one onto a different piece of cloth and cut it out.

Our two geese lived in the yard outside the back door. They made a lot of noise, especially when someone strange came by. Once one of them tore the hem of Aunt Polly's dress. She gave me the piece of cloth for my quilt.

Grandmother laid each animal on a square or rectangle of fabric and chose other scraps for scenery and the border. Then she pinned all of the pieces in place.

Our pigs did nothing much all day but roll in the mud. My father said our big black pig was an excellent specimen.

Grandmother worked out how many squares she needed to make her dolls' quilt. Then she sewed one square at a time. She removed the pins on part of the animal, turned under the edge of the fabric and sewed it to the background. Then she did the same on another part, until that square was finished.

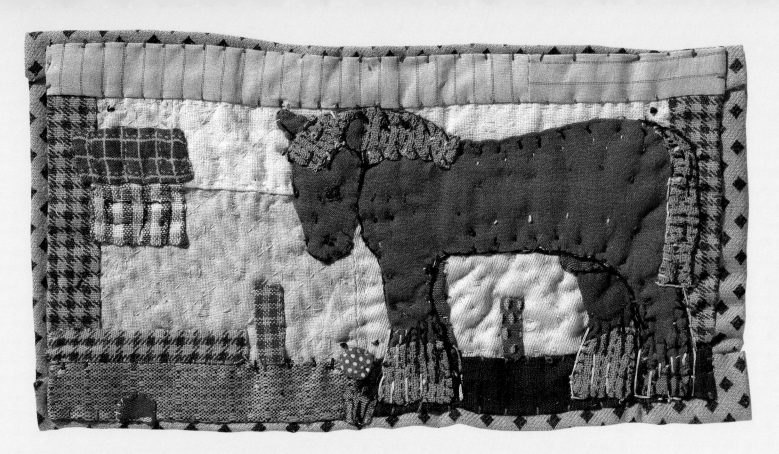

Our shire horse was always busy. He pulled the plough and the cart that took us into town to buy groceries and supplies for the farm. On Sundays we put on our best clothes and went to church in the cart. Our horse waited patiently under a tree until we were ready to return home.

One time my grandmother's friend Marge came over with some scraps of cloth that were perfect for the goat Grandmother wanted on her quilt. The two of them sewed into the night.

My favourite animal of all was our goat Billie.
We had four goats, and she was the best
eater, munching more grass than all the
others together. She also gave the smoothest
and most delicious milk.

When each square was finished, Grandmother laid it on a big piece of unbleached cotton cloth and pinned it in place. She started with the big centre piece of her brother and herself feeding the chickens.

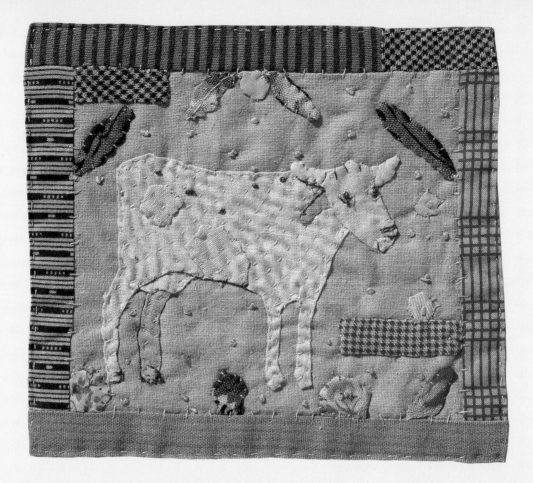

Our cow gave good milk too. She stayed in the
meadow all day, chewing her cud. Each year
she gave birth to a beautiful white calf that
was as frisky as a pony.

After she had pinned each square in place, Grandmother turned the edges under and sewed it down. She used a simple hemming stitch, and you could see her stitches. She attached each piece one at a time until she had sewn all of them to the cotton cloth.

*When the moon came up, I went back into our
house and helped Mother with the supper.
Later I lay in my bed listening to the hoot-
hoot of the owl and thinking about when I
would be old enough to share memories with
my children and grandchildren.*

When it was finished, the quilt kept Grandmother's dolls warm and snug for many years. When she was grown up, Grandmother gave it to her own children for their dolls, and now it is mine. I will always remember Grandmother's story about where it came from and how it was made.

The Patchwork Quilt

Patchwork or appliqué is the technique of cutting out shapes from one piece of fabric and sewing them onto another. The patchwork squares or blocks are then sewn onto a bigger piece of fabric to make a quilt. Sometimes a layer of padding such as an old sheet or blanket is placed between the two layers for added warmth and weight.

Quilting has been a popular activity through the ages and in all parts of the British Isles and the Commonwealth. Very young children were taught to make quilts, beginning by threading the needles and advancing to quite intricate patterns. Poor women made quilts of old clothes and blankets in order to keep warm while middle-class women made more decorative bedcovers. Soldiers used their old uniforms to create colourful quilts.

A favourite pastime was the quilting club or party. People sat together around a big wooden frame and worked on the same quilt. When the quilt was finished it was moved aside and the party began!